IN THE SKY

by Franklin Russell

Illustrated by Frederic Sweney

Copyright © 1965 by Franklin Russell
Illustrations copyright © 1965 by Holt, Rinehart and Winston, Inc.
Library of Congress Catalog Card Number 65-14149
Printed in the United States of America
All rights reserved   4-9772-2515
6618

The Young Hawk

The Hunter was born high in an old hemlock tree. At first, he had been a red-blotched egg, lying in a rough, bulky nest made of sticks and leaves lodged in the crotch of a limb. Beside his egg were two others. His mother, the red-tailed hawk, kept them warm day and night for thirty-one days. On the thirty-second day, the Hunter—naked, squirming and vigorous—smashed through his shell and flopped clear of the broken pieces. He did not then resemble a hawk. His eyes were tightly shut, his beak was soft and only bluntly hooked, and his gangling pale-colored legs and his tiny wing stubs hardly looked capable of developing into the limbs of one of the forest's greatest hunters.

But he was a hawk, a red-tailed hawk. In his tiny body was all the vigor that would sustain him in a life of hunting. The next day, when a brother and sister broke through their shells, the parent red-tails began to search the countryside for choice morsels to feed the nestlings.

The Hunter was reared at first on tiny scraps of meat, worms and beetles. He ate everything offered him. He swayed back and forth with the intensity of his hunger, blindly seizing every morsel. He gulped it down, then gaped for more.

Even at this stage of his life, he was showing his strength and determination. It was a law of the nest that the parent birds did not coddle a nestling. The young bird that gaped widest and cried loudest got the food. The Hunter was competing for the food with his brother and sister, and he got more than either of them. His voice was the loudest, his impatience the greatest. Despite his blind, squirming helplessness at the bottom of the nest, he jostled his brother and sister as he gaped for the first piece of food. He was soon noticeably bigger than either of them.

At night, when the tree swayed and creaked in the wind, he stirred uneasily under his mother's protective feathers. His senses told him dimly that there was a strange and frightening world outside the nest. Within days, his eyes opened and his beak darkened. He soon was standing erect and his piping voice came close to a scream when he was hungry.

Daily his range of vision extended until he could see beyond the nest. He often saw one of his parents watching over the nest from a bare branch of a nearby tree. Although the view above was blocked by the thick foliage of the hemlock, he could see treetops stretching away from the nest on all sides. Sometimes he could see one of his parents soaring in the distance.

Already the hawk nestlings had all the qualities which would govern the rest of their lives. The Hunter's sister was active and aggressive, though she lacked his size and strength. The Hunter's brother was quiet, almost gentle and submissive. Frequently he was knocked aside at feeding time and got nothing to eat. He cried least and slept longest. He seemed to lack both the strength and the desire to assert himself. In a hawk's life, this could be a fatal flaw.

The plumage of the young hawks at first was downy white with dark streaks on the abdomen that formed a broad band of dark gray; the gray tail was crossed by about eight black bars. This plumage soon changed to blotches of dark feathers.

The Hunter was the first to stand on the edge of the nest, peer over and test the strength of his limbs. His sister was close behind him, flapping her wings and spreading them widely in the wind. The third young hawk appeared to be afraid. He remained in the central hollow of the nest and looked around him uncertainly. Then, inspired by the example of his brother and sister, he scrambled to the edge of the nest and looked fearfully downward.

One morning, the three young birds stood expectantly in bright sunlight, looking all around them and stretching their wings in the light breeze. This was the day for flying and each of them felt the urge to leave the nest. At midmorning, their mother arrived with a mouse. As she swung round a tree to approach the nest, the Hunter reached out and screamed for his share of the meal. He could not restrain himself. Facing into the wind, he felt his wings biting into it and lifting him. In a second, he was aloft, propelling himself toward his mother.

She swerved past him and landed on the edge of the nest. Unable to turn back, he glided and faltered and glided, then flapped his wings hard and rose clumsily into the wind. He cried out, half in fear, half in defiance.

A tall hemlock loomed up before him. Unable to avoid it, he crashed into its fragrant green branches and fell through them. He desperately caught a twig with one talon and ended his flight upside down, beating his wings frantically.

When he righted himself, he found that he was surrounded by thick greenery. Immediately the memory of food and the nest banished his fright. He launched himself blindly into the sunlight, but instead of flying into the wind, he now flew with it and was carried quickly down through the trees to blunder into another tree.

He raged at his inability to get back to the nest. He cried out repeatedly. Suddenly his father loomed up with a young bird in his beak. In his eagerness to take the food from his father, the Hunter dropped it into the cool shade. His father flew away. This increased the Hunter's impatience and made him bolder. He hopped from branch to branch till he stood at the top of the tree. All around him, the treetops swayed and sighed in the spring air.

In a distant tree, the Hunter saw his sister and brother. The sister was jumping up and down, half flying and half gliding, but keeping herself constantly above the nest. Suddenly she jumped very high and a gust of wind caught her so that she rose clear of the nest. She disappeared far down the slope, flying strongly at last and crying out loudly. The mother hawk, watching from a nearby tree, now followed the young bird till she beat clumsily into a clump of foliage.

Now alone in the nest, the other young hawk watched the sky anxiously. He cried out when he saw flying shapes through the treetops, thinking they were his parents. But they were crows and they turned sharply on hearing the hawk's voice. Crows hated all hawks and rarely did they find a hawk so helpless as this young one in the nest. The female crow swooped down menacingly and the young hawk reared back and hissed. Then the male crow dived. The young hawk was terrified. He flapped frantically and fell over the edge of the nest, dropping steeply among the hemlocks.

Unlike the other young hawks, he did not settle in a tree.

His fright sent him gliding far down the slope of the valley. His wings were tiring rapidly. When a thick line of trees loomed up ahead, he turned awkwardly, then found himself gliding between the close walls of a steep-sided ravine. He cried out to the narrow slit of sky above, but scarcely a muf-fled echo of his cry reached the bright forest. His parents would neither miss him nor search for him.

The second phase in the Hunter's young life now began. As he became strong enough to fly freely, his fierceness and confidence increased. He was a close copy of his parents, lighter-colored and not so lean perhaps, but slightly bigger than either of them. As he gained strength, he followed his parents in their hunting.

He flew with his father one morning over the valley. The older bird flew into the rising sun, turning slowly in one direction and then another while closely watching the ground. The Hunter kept slightly below and behind him. Presently they settled near the top of a maple tree. The young Hunter copied his father, standing tall and still in the

slanting sun-rays. Both birds moved their heads very slowly to survey all the terrain around them. The Hunter did not know what he was looking for. But he did know he was born to be a watcher. He saw beetles moving slowly through the grass. He saw butterflies flying across sunlit clearings. He saw a frog on a nearby branch.

Suddenly his father was off his perch and swooping down through the trees. In a sprawl of wings, he landed in some long grass and immediately rose again, bearing the kicking body of a large frog. Instantly the young Hunter was at his father's head, screaming loudly and hungrily. The big birds clashed wings as they landed together on a nearby branch. The older bird gave the frog to the Hunter and he gulped it down.

Within days, the Hunter could feed himself. He discovered the nerve-tingling thrill of successful hunting in which hunger spurred him to be patient, fierce and bold. He learned to prowl through the grasses near a swamp, picking up scores of worms, beetles and frogs. He ate almost everything. He became so absorbed in hunting that he sometimes did not see his parents for days. Soon he drifted away from them completely and began exploring his own hunting territory. He learned where food was easiest to find and where many dangers lay. But he could not suspect, in experiencing this marvelous new life force, all the hidden dangers of it.

His sister had already become a victim of her inexperience in hunting. Having found many small snakes living in a swamp near the tree of her birth, she had at first been scared by their writhing bodies and hissing mouths. Later she learned to attack them and ate three or four of them daily.

One day, as she dropped down to a forest clearing, she saw a large snake below her. Its body was protruding from the ground the length of the hawk's outstretched wing. She seized the lean, black body. Instantly she was knocked off her feet as the snake violently coiled his powerful length. One coil flipped over the hawk's head and tightened round her neck. She flapped her wings desperately and rolled over. The long grass wound round her neck, trapping both creatures. The hawk could not free herself. The snake could not draw himself to safety in the ground. For several hours the two creatures struggled. The sun climbed higher in the sky. The young hawk gasped. Frequently she struggled more violently, only to become increasingly more weak. In the midafternoon, she died. Soon after, the snake, feeling the tension gone from the hawk's body, managed to uncoil himself and slide deep underground.

The Great Migration

As the warmth went out of the summer, the Hunter began to sit motionless for long hours in an old pine tree. Sixty days had now passed since that momentous morning when he had left the nest. He wakened before dawn each day and remained still and silent, facing the red horizon and the rising sun. The glowing light revealed his hooded amber eyes, the curving thrust of his beak, his powerful, sleek and mottled body and the broad red-tinged fan of his tail.

In the early hours, the hawk was a watcher. As he looked down across the sweep of the valley before him, he saw clearly every visible creature. He watched with eyesight so powerful that he could see distant spiders on webs and beetles scuttling over leaves far below.

He saw a pair of ducks floating silently down the valley on their way to a lake or pond where they would eat. He saw a mouse on a stone twitching his whiskers and licking his paws as he basked in the early morning sun. He saw shafts of light piercing branches of an old tree where a squirrel was jerkily climbing. When the squirrel saw the hawk, one of his great enemies, he warned the forest of the danger with his agitated *zick-zick-zick* call.

The squirrel's warning cries were sharp and constant. The sun was now a full, rich orb rising rapidly over the horizon. The hawk flexed his yellow legs, hunched his back and suddenly launched himself into space. He burst out of the sheltering leaves and briefly merged with the greenery of a mass of beeches before him. Then, with a sweep of mottled wing, he curved majestically clear of the forest and began climbing. He was unaccountably restless. He no longer hunted with his summer energy. He flew into a current of sharply cooler air and whistled softly. Some drastic change was coming into his life. He was impatient for it to begin.

One morning, soon after the leaves around him were tinged with yellow, he saw circling birds appearing in the northern sky. He rose to meet them, and by midday was flying among

them. They were broad-winged hawks, smaller than he, with widely-banded tails. They drifted south, but the Hunter did not stay with them. He turned back and dropped to his watching place.

The flights of migrating birds thickened as the days shortened and grew cooler. On some days, a thousand hawks passed by. The Hunter was excited by this pageant of flight but still was not ready to join it. Whatever the mysterious force that makes birds migrate, it held him obedient in its grip. He would scream suddenly at lines of crows pumping overhead. He would fly back and forth restlessly. Sometimes he would poise himself at a great height above the migrants, and for no apparent reason, let himself fall steeply among them. Once when he dived into a thick flight of swallows, they turned and twisted in confusion.

He watched a pair of peregrine falcons having sport with the migrants one day. A male falcon, perhaps the fastest and most skillful flier in the air, drove himself at high speed parallel to a fleeing sparrow. The falcon accurately matched the sparrow's every twist and turn so that the two creatures looked like one bird lancing across the sky. Then, without effort, and still flying at top speed, the falcon reached out one claw and plucked his victim out of mid-air.

The migration time quickened the Hunter's blood and sharpened his senses. When a lone hawk came into view one morning, circling lazily, the Hunter screamed at him from a tree. The second hawk was also a red-tail and the Hunter felt a strange new force inside him. It lifted him into the air and sent him towards the other hawk. The instinct to fight was strong. The two birds swerved at each other. The Hunter ripped and tore at the gasping, squealing bird before him, then felt himself gripped in a steely talon. With a vicious counterattack he wrenched himself free and ripped feathers from the other hawk's chest. At the same time, the two birds were falling steadily. With a final snapping of beaks, they broke away almost at treetop level. The migrant hawk then

went his way to the south and the Hunter rose high in the air to watch for new arrivals.

Soon after dawn the next day, he rose and joined a loose-knit band of hawks which had appeared out of the north. Once flying with them, he whistled twice in excitement, knowing that the powerful urge inside him was now being satisfied.

These were supreme days in the lives of all migrant birds. Thousands of them were now in the air at once, visible from horizon to horizon, drifting, wheeling, speeding or gliding their way to the south. The migrants moved in infinitely diverse ways. Long lines of ducks and occasional V-shaped flights of geese decorated the sky. Their flight leaders honked warnings when they saw the hawks.

Wings fluttered in treetops as small birds moved south. Many of them fed by day and waited for night to take to the air in thousands.

A peregrine falcon, hovering over a flight of ducks, dropped straight down and struck one of them. The violent impact killed the duck instantly, and it fell in a convulsive flutter of wings. But the falcon did not attempt to follow his victim. For some, migration is a tragedy, for others a grim kind of sport.

The hawks passed easily over lakes and rivers and the Hunter saw the forest thinning as rolling hill country spread out beneath him. All during the day, the size of the hawk flight grew as birds rose to join the migrants.

At dusk that day, the hawks dropped to earth, falling slowly and widely spread. For the first time in many months, the Hunter found himself in new territory. He landed warily in a group of hickories as the dusk began to settle across the earth. The western sky was blood red and the air pressure was falling rapidly. This made the Hunter restless. He knew a storm was imminent. He slept fitfully that night. The sky opened and closed with racing black clouds passing the moon, and gusts of wind blew restlessly. Wild calls came out of the darkness and hurtling black shapes etched themselves against the sky. A duck squawked overhead so loudly that the Hunter jerked up his head. A flash of lightning silhouetted a group of ducks against the sky for a moment, then they disappeared.

Soon after midnight it began raining. Glistening drops of moisture collected on the Hunter's oily black feathers and ran down to his broad fantail. Eventually, when the wind rose and shook the trees violently, he abandoned sleep and remained hunched and miserable on his branch, awaiting the dawn.

By the time the sky lightened, the wind was near gale force. The Hunter rose and was propelled rapidly southeastward, riding the wind on bowed wings. As he swept over the trees, other hawks rose to join him. Harsh cries, piercing whistles and screams fled downwind as the host of hawks took to the turbulent air. The fast flying excited the Hunter and he gave a long, penetrating whistle.

Other birds of prey rose to fly together under the lowering sky—broad-winged hawks, rough-legged hawks, sharp-shinned hawks and red-shouldered hawks. The white crown of a bald eagle showed starkly as he turned in the wind. The

Hunter flew briefly near him and could see his fierce curving beak and the cold gleam in his eye. The eagle turned against the wind and rose into the air. Then he was gone in a rush of speed.

Only the most powerful fliers flew comfortably during the gale. Flocks of smaller migrants were sent tumbling briefly in sudden gusts of wind. Because they could not glide back and forth like the hawks, the smaller birds were tossed about in the force of the wind.

When the hawks settled that night, the wind grew stronger. As the Hunter crouched down against a blast of wind, he had a fleeting glimpse of a body hurtling by and heard the scrabbling of feet as a small bird came to rest. Some of the birds hit treetops and were injured as they let themselves down into the forest. The night-migrating creatures squawked with anxiety and fear in the dark and blustering sky as they tried to cope with the storm. Most of them stayed in shelter, but those that took to the air found themselves in a nightmare of wind and rain.

Throughout the storm, the Hunter stayed awake. He hunched forward, his eyes half hooded, and looked without fear into the black night. Suddenly the *kee-r-r-ing* call of another red-tail sounded from the gloom. He listened intently, but the cry was gone in a moment.

Shortly before dawn, the wind diminished. As the sky lightened, the Hunter launched himself into the wind and soared rapidly above the treeline. He flew with the grayish beginnings of dawn appearing at his left shoulder. He was tired, but he would continue the migration.

In this way, the flight south continued through the days of the fall. The Hunter was a tiny speck of life in a living parade of creatures that stretched for hundreds of miles from north to south. The land rolled beneath him day after day as he crossed rivers and soared above the length of a range of hills, gliding through the air without once flapping his wings. He crossed a huge marshland and then an estuary. The land grew constantly greener and the weather warmer.

He would not experience the snow and ice that would shortly grip the land of his birth, and he would soon reach his winter hunting territory. He had never seen this new land. But his mysterious instinct would unerringly guide him to a spot where he would hunt until spring. Then he would head back north again toward the familiar land of the hemlocks where he was born.

Return

At the first faint sign of spring, the Hunter felt the urge to return north. He was greatly changed. He was now a superbly confident adult bird of prey. He had spent a winter of winds and rains in a southern valley near the sea. He had become cunning in his ground hunting, having spent many days prowling through grass and scrub in search of field mice, beetles, frogs, snakes and young rabbits. He had discovered the helplessness of many ground creatures when they were confronted by a bird which could pursue them on foot or drop on them from the air.

Now he felt a new hunger growing in him. He had been the creation of his parents, and now he must re-create himself.

He flew north, allowing his flight to be controlled by the weather. The wind blew from the south and he rode on its wings. Then the wind blew from the land and carried him toward the shimmering line of the ocean in the distance. The rains fell and he spent two days in a valley, eating sparsely of mice and frogs in the swamp there. During his northern flight, he watched for other red-tailed hawks but saw none. A pair of older birds—perhaps they were his parents—flew by one day and he whistled at them. But they ignored him and flew on north. Like all adult red-tails, they knew where they would nest. They had used the same nest for five years.

He continued his flight northward through occasional rain and lightly drifting snow. He passed over thousands of small migrant warblers, working their way north through forest and scrub. From just before dawn, when song birds called loudly all around him, until dusk, when the first owl calls rose above the forest, he pressed northward.

One bright day, he passed over the area where he had been born. His father saw him from a point high in the sky. His mother, motionless in a maple tree, watched him pass. But to them the young hawk was now a stranger.

The Hunter paused in his northward flight, remembering the good hunting grounds in the valley below. Immediately his father fell like a thunderbolt from the sky and forced the young hawk to keep moving. In the breeding season, he was learning, each hawk occupied his own fixed territory.

One day, however, there were no birds to harry him. The air was calm. He paused on the pinnacle of an updraft. Below, he saw a swamp where he knew there would be a rich harvest of frogs and snakes. A river sparkled in the distance; there would be good hunting along its banks. The ground was lightly forested, and in the open patches between the clumps of trees there would be rabbits.

He spent most of the day standing on a bare branch in a pine tree, surveying the new land. The thick forest teemed with life. Chickadees, nuthatches, vireos and robins called incessantly. From the swamp, he heard the muted cries of red-winged blackbirds. A great flock of them had settled there at the end of their migration. Suddenly, he felt a great surge of exultation. This was his land, his new home. He launched himself from the pine and beat his way into the south wind. He was a master of the air. No other bird could match his soaring sweeps across the invisible wind currents. He knew their shape and substance, even though he could not see them. He became excited by updrafts—columns of vertically-rising warm air or winds deflected diagonally upwards from mountainside or hills.

The rising sun was warming the earth. The Hunter flew steadily across the valley toward a low line of yellow cliffs, where, he knew, there would be an updraft. The sun had now suffused the land with light. It blazed on the yellow cliffs, now almost directly below the hawk. Suddenly he felt the first updraft. It caught his wide wings, bowed them and sent him buoyantly upward. This shaft of air had all the warmth and vitality of a living thing.

The valley was shrinking but the world was expanding under the hawk's eyes. A rolling sweep of forest spread out on all sides, broken by the winding lines of streams, the pock-marks of ponds and swamps, the wavering marks of hills and mounds. The horizon was gradually becoming a circle of gray. The hawk continued to rise, climbing toward the blue dome of the sky which, every minute, was fading in the growth of the new day.

The column of warm air lifting the hawk had already met masses of colder air above. Wisps of cloud, or water vapor, appeared. His excitement rose suddenly. He whistled piercingly—*keeee-keeeeee*—and the muffling cloud of vapor absorbed the sharp sound.

At this great height, no creature could see the red-tailed hawk in his lonely climb. But he could still see the earth stretched out below in patterns of mottled greens and grays.

Presently he had risen so high that the earth disappeared and he was alone in silent clouds. For hours now, he had not flapped his wings. It was becoming cold and the updraft had wavered to an odd and feeble puff of warm air. He glided south in search of another updraft. He passed over and beyond the clouds. A long lake stretched across the southern horizon, reflecting a vivid slash of light.

Then, as the sun descended, he began sinking slowly to earth. He widened his sweeps across the sky. His hunger, unnoticed before, now sharpened and he steepened his descent so that the earth expanded hugely in detail. At the same time, the sun sank swiftly into a clouded, reddening western sky. One moment he was starkly lighted in its rays; the next moment he was bathed in a soft orange glow. Then suddenly he was below its direct light altogether and dropping toward the darkening earth.

Above him, the lowest clouds were turning pale yellow. They quickly became transformed into a rich amber, while, still higher, other layers of cloud glowed with colors of orange and gold.

The hawk swept high over the rim of his valley and headed down toward a dead branch on top of an old pine tree far in the distance. This was to become his favorite watching post.

The uprushing wind of his descent murmured across his wings, and his amber eyes stared down to pick out the smallest details below. He saw cottontail rabbits in the flat, clear grassland near a marsh. He watched them stand stiff as sentinels for a moment, then scatter like thistledown in a high wind, perhaps because they saw him.

The bare-limbed pine was now in sight, but still far away. The hawk saw it against the hillside the same instant he caught a fleeting glimpse of a very tall hare standing against some dried grass in a forest clearing. All during the hawk's daylong flight, the hare had remained in his grass refuge and had only just emerged to feed in the greater safety of twilight. He saw the hawk but did not run.

Although the hawk saw the hare clearly, he did not alter his line of flight or miss a wingbeat. He passed behind some beeches and landed lightly in the enveloping greenery. He turned and faced out over the slope of the valley. He was now following his habit of the hunt. Lacking the speed and agility to seize a running animal, he must catch him through cunning. His hunger was now a nagging pain inside him.

He launched himself in the direction of the hare, flying low and fast. The frantic *zick-zick-zick* of a squirrel warned the forest creatures as the frightened animal had a horrifying, closeup glimpse of the Hunter winging over him. But the hawk ignored him.

The blunt tops of some hemlocks shot past him and suddenly the Hunter was within sight of the hare's clearing. He banked between two beeches to make a diagonal approach that would give him the most benefit of cover before he burst into sight. As he flew, he caught a glimpse of his expected victim through the low branches, loping along slowly and leaning forward to nibble patches of grass. As the hawk swung

around the last concealing tree, the hare rose on his haunches, sniffed the evening air and stiffened. The hawk was a fleeting apparition of silence now, flying low and fast, his eyes staring and his curved beak open to seize the hare. In the last second of the attack, his long yellow legs swung out from under him and he flung his wings back to concentrate the entire power of his strike into the tips of his talons.

The hare's first sight of the approaching hawk was the great outspread wings behind him. As the deadly feet swung down, the hare contorted his muscles convulsively and made the greatest leap of his life, a leap so fast and so long that the hawk was forced to swerve in the last moment of his strike. He struck vainly at the fleeing animal, felt one talon catch, then thumped into a clump of grass and rolled, wings sprawling. He was up in an instant. He heaved himself aloft for another try, but the hare had gone. Not even the scuff of the hare's flying feet sounded in the soft evening air.

Hawk Meets His Mate

In his new territory, the Hunter spent many hours in tree-tops, always facing south. The incredible instinct that had sent him south for the winter and had brought him north in the spring was now working on him in another way. He seemed to know that his mate would come from the south and he awaited her arrival with growing impatience.

Soon after dawn one day, he saw the dark speck of a hawk circling on the southern horizon. The sun rose and the bird appeared distinctly in the light. The Hunter launched himself and flew steadily toward the circling bird. The traveler saw him immediately and began lofting higher. The Hunter followed.

He recognized with excitement that this was a female. Her flight meant she knew her pursuer was a male. The two birds were soon a symphony of wingbeats rising quickly in a morning updraft. They swung rhythmically across the sky, first one way, then another, as though flying with identical intentions.

By midday, they had disappeared from the sight of any ground creature. Towering masses of cloud rose around them. Through rifts in the cloud, the earth seemed remote.

The two birds did not return to earth until evening. Both were famished and tired. They headed through the dusk to the swamp where the male bird knew there was food. The female followed him closely in his low sweep across the flat-lands clamorous with the sound of singing frogs newly

emerged from their winter sleep. Suddenly he dropped. The female swerved to join him. Their arrival set a group of frogs leaping frantically in all directions. The two big birds ate as many frogs as they could catch.

Over the ensuing days, the hawks hunted the new land together. They seemed devoted to each other and would likely breed and fly together until death separated them. Frequently on stormy spring days, they would rise and hurtle across the sky in mad displays of flying which seemed to express their exhilaration together. Long before the beeches, oaks, or maples began to show tinges of green in their branches, the hawks were ready to nest.

Because both birds were one year old, instinct guided their urge to nest. The female was unsure. She searched the tree-tops for a nesting place. Hour by hour she flew back and forth dropping sticks in the high forks of trees. Usually the sticks slipped to earth and she continued her efforts.

In the top of a hemlock tree she found an old mass of sticks and twigs which had been used by great horned owls the previous year. She dropped a stick on it, saw that it settled, and then flew away to get more.

In the next five days, as both birds worked gathering sticks, the nest grew quickly. The ground beneath it was strewn with fallen sticks, but the nest became four feet wide and nearly two feet deep. As the nest grew, the female collected feathers from some of her victims and lined the hollow in the middle of the nest. Occasionally, she laid the bodies of mice around the edge of the nest as though in anticipation of the arrival of nestling hawks. The mice were to be eaten later.

When the work was finally finished, she broke off two sprays of pine foliage from a nearby tree and placed them at the edge of the nest. During the nest building, eggs had been developing inside her body. She was now ready to lay her eggs.

When the male red-tail returned from the swamp one morning, he found his mate sitting in the center of the nest, her feathers fluffed out and her broad fantail spread widely. Her body was moving strangely. He called her quietly—*churrr-churrr*—but she did not respond. He flew back to the swamp. When he returned to the nest later, the female had gone. Lying in the nest hollow was a lone egg, splotched and starkly white. In two days, two more eggs joined the first.

From a dead limb in the topmost branches of a tall hemlock near the nest, the male hawk now spent much time watching the valley below. Perched there, he watched for food and also for enemies that might threaten his hunting ground and his nest.

The Hunter remembered what he saw, but so did other animals. One evening, a weasel paused at the foot of the hawk's hemlock and lifted her sharp face to sniff the air. Then she silently climbed the tree. Under the hawk's nest, she paused again. When the female hawk moved restlessly on the nest, the weasel turned and went down to the ground again. But she remembered.

On another day, a crow flew over the hawk's nest as the female settled on her eggs. The crow did not change the slow pace of his flying as he disappeared over the trees. But he too remembered. Now the survival of the Hunter's brood would depend on the quality of his instinct and of his memory against those of the crow and the weasel.

While the female brooded, the Hunter caught mice and frogs and fed them to her on the nest. When she went hunting, he settled into the hollow and warmed the eggs. His watching of the nest was so constant there was scarcely an instant that the eggs were left unguarded. But vigilance and instinct and memory are never perfect.

One of the eggs was moving vigorously. Soon a young hawk broke through the shell. The female hawk left the nest and glided through the trees. The Hunter, too, had left his post.

Swiftly the black figure of a crow in a distant tree took wing and flew silently toward the nest. The crow, which had been watching, landed on the nest and reached forward to spear the nestling. But cunning as he was, his instinct was also imperfect. His senses were so occupied by the prospect of food that he did not immediately see the Hunter returning. The Hunter's first glimpse of the black bird on his nest enraged him. The crow scarcely had time to swing into the air before he was struck in mid-flight and hurled deeply among the branches. His cawing cries of panic were cut short by the Hunter's talons clenching his head.

After the other two eggs hatched, the hawks began a fever of hunting to feed the nestlings. This was the most vulnerable time of the nesting period. The helpless young hawks, lying naked in the nest, needed fine-shredded food and constant protection. Once, a crow, visible as a shapeless blob of black

feathers, settled in a far tree. Instantly the Hunter flew after him and the two birds fled across the forest, their cries of mutual hatred fading in the distance.

As the Hunter ranged widely and alone across the country, he saw other birds hunting with an intensity that matched his own.

The Hunter saw a duck struggling in the shallows of a marsh pool, as though injured and unable to fly. Without hesitation, he closed his wings and fell sheerly to the marsh, the wind whistling through his feathers. As he fell, he saw the duck still struggling, but he also saw a motionless animal nearby. It was a fox. The hawk pulled out of his dive with a harsh rustle of disturbed air and landed gracefully on the top of a tree. The fox looked up at him. The duck stopped flapping. Then the fox turned and disappeared into the undergrowth. The duck took off and fled, quacking. She had been pretending a broken wing to lure the fox away from her nest.

Danger was everywhere for all nesting birds. Nestlings were the favorite food of scores of hunters. Crows, terrified

that he would plunder their nests, frequently attacked the Hunter himself. On several occasions, these attacks were so vicious that he was forced to flip over on his back in mid-flight and meet the attacks with his talons. A pair of king-birds—white-chested, blue-headed flycatchers—each not much bigger than the hawk's head, rose rapidly beneath him, calling angrily and urgently. Their attack was so persistent that he was forced to rise and leave them far below.

Even the Hunter feared an attack on his nest. One morning, when a bald eagle came closer than usual to the hawk's nest, slowly wheeling, the Hunter watched intently from his lookout. The big bird came still closer. The Hunter rose swiftly with a loud scream, and the eagle turned slowly to meet the attack. The Hunter rose rapidly above him, folded his wings and came down in a rush. Just as the two big birds were about to collide, the eagle flipped his seven feet of wings and turned on his back, exactly as the Hunter had done in the crow attack. The Hunter shot past the reaching talons, but climbed again frantically till he was above the eagle. Down he came again in a streaking dive. The eagle rolled over and spread his talons to ward off the attack. This attacking and climbing went on as both birds drifted away to the east. Finally the eagle dropped away steeply from the Hunter and slid down over the forest at terrific speed, his head a tiny beacon of white against the blurred green of the trees. The Hunter did not attempt to follow him.

As the young hawks grew rapidly, the Hunter became doubly wary. Their size and their noisy cries made them conspicuous. In five days, they doubled their size and weight, and passed quickly from pink helplessness to downy vigor. Soon they were standing up, gawky and banded with gray.

At dusk one day, the weasel returned to the tree to make another attempt to raid the hawk's nest. Even though the Hunter was standing motionless in a nearby tree, he did not see the shadowy weasel moving silently up the tree. He did not see the animal's tiny face peering over the edge of the nest, or see him staring at the nearest nestling. But he did see a sudden flurry of young birds, leaping in terror from a danger they instinctively recognized. One of the nestlings lunged desperately from the nest and fell from the tree.

The weasel, unsure now, snaked down the tree trunk. The two nestlings who still remained in the nest were screaming. The Hunter beat clumsily around the tree, seeking the weasel, but he was no match for her lithe speed. The weasel dashed away to safety through the trees and scared a young hare hiding in a thicket, which bolted in panic. Although the baby hawk on the ground cried out repeatedly, his parents ignored him. They brought food to the nest, and the two remaining hawklets fed ravenously. There was no instinct in the Hunter or his mate to take care of the nestling struggling on the ground below the tree. During the night, the weasel returned for the third time and claimed the tiny victim on the ground.

Days later, the two young hawks left the nest together one morning and flew into the trees. All around them was a growing horde of young birds. Woodpeckers and wood ducks piped from holes in trees; ducklings followed their mothers in the marsh; young birds called for food from all levels of the forest.

The trees were filled with caterpillars, newly-emerged beetles, freshly-hatched mosquitoes and flies. The ponds swarmed with thousands of young tadpoles and frogs. This was early summer's time of plenty.

The young hawks soon found their places in it. They became absorbed, as their parents had before them, in extracting their own living from the forest. They saw less and less of their parents. The two adult birds would often disappear into the blue sky, and occasionally a faint shrill scream would sound from the clouds. The red-tailed hawk and his mate had answered the urge to re-create and were triumphant.